CHRISTMAS CAROLS

Arranged by Marjorie Wyckoff
Pictures by Corinne Malvern

GOLDEN PRESS
NEW YORK

Seventeenth Printing, 1969

© Copyright 1946 by Western Publishing Company, Inc.
Printed in the U.S.A.

O Jesu Sweet, O Jesu Mild

Scheidt's Tablaturbuch, *1650*
"*O Jesulein suss, O Jesulein mild*"

Scheidt's Tablaturbuch, *1650*
Harmonization by J. S. Bach, 1685-1750 (Simplified)

O   Je - su   sweet,   O   Je - su

mild, O love - ly Babe, Ce - les - tial

Child! Thou cam'st to us from Heav'n a -

bove To bring poor mor - tals God's great

love O Je - su sweet, O Je - su mild!

O Jesu sweet, O Jesu mild,
Help us to do Thy holy will.
Lo, all our lives are Thine alone,
Since, in our hearts, Thy love
    has shone.
O Jesu sweet, O Jesu mild.

Away in a Manger

Martin Luther

German Folk Song

A - way in a man - ger, no crib for a bed, The lit - tle Lord Je - sus laid down His sweet head; The stars in the sky Looked down where He lay, The lit - tle Lord Je - sus, A - sleep in the hay.

The cattle are lowing, the poor Baby wakes,
But little Lord Jesus no crying He makes;
I love Thee, Lord Jesus! look down from the sky,
And stay by my cradle till morning is nigh.

Deck the Halls

Traditional

Old Welsh Melody

Deck the halls with bows of hol - ly, Fa, la, la, la, la, la, la, la, la. 'Tis the sea - son to be jol - ly, Fa, la, la, la, la, la, la, la, la. Don we now our gay ap-par - el, Fa, la, la, la, la, la, la, la, la. Troll the an-cient yule-tide car-ol, Fa, la, la, la, la, la, la, la, la.

See the blazing Yule before us,
Fa, la, la, la, la, la, la, la, la.
Strike the harp and join the chorus,
Fa, la, la, la, la, la, la, la, la.

Follow me in merry measure,
Fa, la, la, la, la, la, la, la, la.
While I tell of Yuletide treasure,
Fa, la, la, la, la, la, la, la, la.

The First Nowell

Words traditional

Traditional English Melody

The first Now - ell the an - gel did say Was to cer-tain poor shep-herds in fields as they lay; In fields where they lay keep-ing their sheep, On a cold win-ter's night that was so deep. Now - ell, Now - ell, Now - ell, Now - ell. Born is the King of Is - ra - el.

Refrain

Joy to the World

From Psalm 92
Isaac Watts, 1719

George Frederick Händel, 1742

11

While Shepherds Watched Their Flocks

Rev. Nathan Tate, 1696 George Frederick Händel

While shep-herds watched their flocks by night, All seat - ed on the ground,__ The an-gel of the Lord came down And glo-ry shone a-round,__ And glo-ry shone a - round.

O Come, All Ye Faithful
(Adeste Fideles)

Anonymous Latin Hymn, 17th or 18th Century
Translated by Fred. Oakley, 1841

J. F. Wades Cantus Diversi, *1751*

O come, all ye faith-ful, joy-ful and tri - umph-ant, O

come ye, O come ye to Beth - le -hem;

Come and be - hold Him, born the King of an - gels;

O come, let us a - dore Him, O come, let us a - dore Him, O

come, let us a - dore Him, — Christ, — the Lord.

He Is Sleeping

George Wolfson

Polish Carol, 16th Century
Arranged by Marjorie M. Wyckoff

Chil - dren, come and see Him slum - ber, In the man - ger soft with hay. He, our bless - ed lit - tle

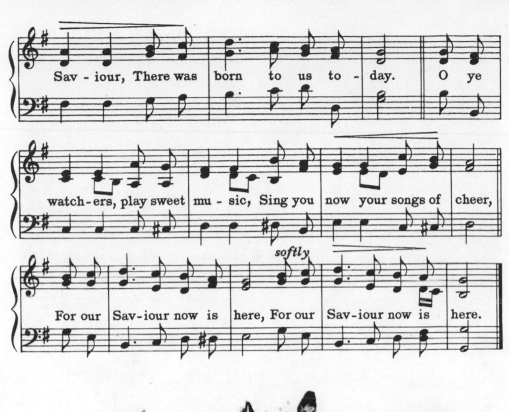

Sav - iour, There was born to us to - day. O ye
watch - ers, play sweet mu - sic, Sing you now your songs of cheer,
softly
For our Sav-iour now is here, For our Sav-iour now is here.

O Christmas Tree

Jane Werner

Traditional German Tune

O Christ - mas tree, O Christ - mas tree, Your gay green dress de - lights us! You do not fade with win - ter's snow, You bloom with lights when cold winds blow. O Christ - mas tree, O Christ-mas tree, Your gay green dress de - lights us.

I Saw Three Ships

Traditional English

Traditional Air from Derbyshire

I saw three ships come sail-ing in, On Christ-mas day, on Christ-mas day, I

saw three ships come sail - ing in, On

Christ - mas day in the morn - ing!

Silent Night

Joseph Mohr
Translator anonymous

Franz Grüber

Si - lent night, Ho - ly night, All is calm,

all is bright. 'Round yon vir - gin Moth - er and Child,

Ho - ly In - fant so ten-der and mild, Sleep in heav - en-ly

peace,_____ Sleep in heav - en-ly peace.___

Hark! the Herald Angels Sing

Charles Wesley   Felix Mendelssohn